Here's all the great literature in this grade level of *Celebrate Reading!*

BOOK A
Under My Hat

Finding a Starting Point

Big Books & Little Books

So Can I
by Allan Ahlberg
✳ CHILDREN'S BOOK AWARD AUTHOR

One Gorilla
by Atsuko Morozumi
✳ *NEW YORK TIMES* BEST ILLUSTRATED

Mary Had a Little Lamb
by Sarah Josepha Hale
Photographs by
Bruce McMillan
✳ ALA NOTABLE ILLUSTRATOR

Featured Poet

David McCord

It's a Perfect Day!
by Abigail Pizer
✳ CHILDREN'S CHOICE AUTHOR

Peanut Butter and Jelly
Illustrations by
Nadine Bernard Westcott
✳ CHILDREN'S CHOICE ILLUSTRATOR

The Gunnywolf
retold and illustrated
by A. Delaney
✳ CHILDREN'S CHOICE

BOOK B
Hurry, Furry Feet

When the Elephant Walks
by Keiko Kasza
✳ ALA NOTABLE AUTHOR

Sitting in My Box
by Dee Lillegard
Illustrations by Jon Agee
✳ NEW YORK TIMES BEST ILLUSTRATOR

Old Hat, New Hat
by Stan and Jan Berenstain
✳ MICHIGAN YOUNG READER
AWARD AUTHORS

The Foot Book and
Hurry, Hurry, Hurry
by Dr. Seuss
✳ CALDECOTT HONOR ILLUSTRATOR
✳ LAURA INGALLS WILDER AWARD
AUTHOR/ILLUSTRATOR

My Street Begins at My House
by Ella Jenkins
Illustrations by
James E. Ransome
✳ PARENTS' CHOICE SONGWRITER

Featured Poet

Evelyn Beyer

Big Book & Little Book

The Wheels on the Bus
by Maryann Kovalski

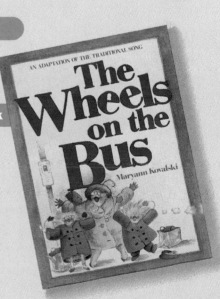

BOOK C
Our Singing Planet

"Pardon?" Said the Giraffe
by Colin West

I Can Make Music
by Eve B. Feldman

The Little Red Hen and the Grain of Wheat
by Sara Cone Bryant

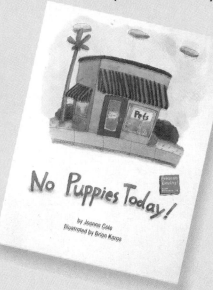

My Mom Travels a Lot
by Caroline Feller Bauer
Illustrations by
Nancy Winslow Parker
❋ CHRISTOPHER AWARD
❋ NEW YORK TIMES BEST ILLUSTRATED

Tommy Meng San
by Belinda Yun-Ying
and Douglas Louie

Featured Poets

N. M. Bodecker
Rowena Bennett
Mary Ann Hoberman
Lee Bennett Hopkins

Big Book & Little Book

No Puppies Today!
by Joanna Cole
Illustrations by Brian Karas
❋ ALA NOTABLE AUTHOR
❋ CHILDREN'S CHOICE AUTHOR
❋ TEACHERS' CHOICE AUTHOR

BOOK D
My Favorite Foodles

The Doorbell Rang
by Pat Hutchins
❋ ALA Notable Children's Book
❋ Children's Choice

Aiken Drum
Traditional Song

**The Great, Big,
Enormous Turnip**
retold by Alexei Tolstoy
Illustrations by
Helen Oxenbury
❋ ALA Notable Illustrator
❋ Kate Greenaway Medal
Illustrator

From Seeds to Zucchinis
by LuLu Delacre

Hello, House!
retold by Linda Hayward
Illustrations by
Lynn Munsinger
❋ New York Times Best Illustrator
❋ Children's Choice

Featured Poets

Eve Merriam
Lucia and James L. Hymes, Jr.
Dennis Lee
John Ciardi
Charlotte Zolotow

Big Book & Little Book

If You Give a Moose a Muffin
by Laura Joffe Numeroff
Illustrations by Felicia Bond
❋ Children's Choice

BOOK E

Happy Faces

Mouse's Marriage
by Junko Morimoto
✳ AUSTRALIAN PICTURE BOOK
OF THE YEAR ILLUSTRATOR

Who Will Bell the Cat?
retold as a play
by Sandy Asher

The Mice Go Marching
by Hap Palmer
✳ PARENTS' CHOICE SONGWRITER

Mama's Birthday Present
by Carmen Tafolla

Baby Rattlesnake
told by TeAta
retold by Lynn Moroney

The Desert
by Carol Carrick
✳ NEW YORK TIMES NOTABLE AUTHOR

It's George!
by Miriam Cohen
Illustrations by Lillian Hoban
✳ CHILDREN'S CHOICE AUTHOR
✳ PARENTS' CHOICE AUTHOR
✳ CHRISTOPHER AWARD ILLUSTRATOR

Featured Poets

Eloise Greenfield
Karla Kuskin
Myra Cohn Livingston

Big Book & Little Book

On the Go
by Ann Morris
Photographs by Ken Heyman

BOOK F

A Canary with Hiccups

Two Greedy Bears
retold by Mirra Ginsburg
Illustrations by
Jose Aruego and Ariane Dewey
✳ ALA NOTABLE AUTHOR
✳ BOSTON GLOBE-HORN
BOOK AWARD ILLUSTRATORS

Eat Up, Gemma
by Sarah Hayes
Illustrations by Jan Ormerod
✳ KATE GREENAWAY
AUTHOR/ILLUSTRATOR TEAM AWARD

A Healthy Day
by Paul Showers
✳ NEW JERSEY INSTITUTE OF
TECHNOLOGY AWARD AUTHOR

Looby Loo
Traditional Song

**Henry and Mudge
and the Forever Sea**
from the story by
Cynthia Rylant
Illustrations by Suçie Stevenson
✳ PARENTING READING MAGIC AWARD
✳ NEWBERY MEDAL AUTHOR

Amazing Pets
by Lynda DeWitt

Fox on the Job
from the story by
James Marshall
✳ ALA NOTABLE CHILDREN'S AUTHOR
✳ READING RAINBOW SELECTION

Do Your Ears Hang Low?
Illustrations by Lois Ehlert
✳ ALA NOTABLE ILLUSTRATOR

Ready...Set...Read!
from the book by Joanna Cole
and Stephanie Calmenson
Illustrations by Lois Ehlert

Featured Poets

Jack Prelutsky
Lee Bennett Hopkins
Shel Silverstein
Gail Kredenser
Zheyna Gay

Big Book & Little Book

The Goat Who Couldn't Sneeze
retold by Cecilia Avalos
Illustrations by Vivi Escrivá

Celebrate Reading!
Big Book Bonus

It Looked Like Spilt Milk
by Charles G. Shaw

Jamberry
by Bruce Degen
✳ CHILDREN'S CHOICE

Skip to My Lou
by Nadine Bernard Westcott
✳ REDBOOK CHILDREN'S
PICTURE BOOK AWARD

Lazy Lion
by Mwenye Hadithi
Illustrations by
Adrienne Kennaway
✳ KATE GREENAWAY MEDAL
ILLUSTRATOR

The Cake That Mack Ate
by Rose Robart
Illustrations by
Maryann Kovalski

The Right Number of Elephants
by Jeff Sheppard

Under My Hat

Titles in This Set

Under My Hat
Hurry, Furry Feet
Our Singing Planet
My Favorite Foodles
Happy Faces
A Canary with Hiccups

About the Cover Artist

The artist Andrew Shachat painted the pictures on the
cover of this book. Mr. Shachat collects toys, especially tin
toys and robots. He says that he gets ideas for his pictures from
his collection.

ISBN 0-673-81121-2

1997
Scott, Foresman and Company, Glenview, Illinois
All Rights Reserved.
Printed in the United States of America.

Acknowledgments appear on page 64.

12345678910DR010099989796

Under My Hat

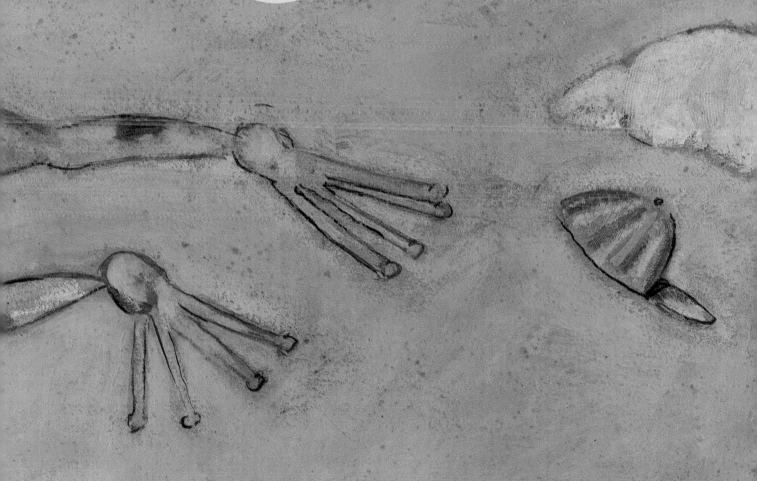

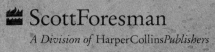
ScottForesman

A Division of HarperCollinsPublishers

A Book to Share

Look at Me

So Can I 8
Fantasy by Allan Ahlberg
Illustrations by Colin McNaughton

One Gorilla 18
Fantasy written and illustrated by
Atsuko Morozumi

A Word from the Author 42
Article by Atsuko Morozumi

Mary Had a Little Lamb 44
Rhyme by Sarah Josepha Hale
Photo-illustrations by Bruce McMillan

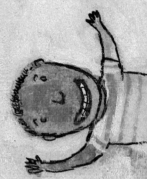

A Word from the Illustrator 56
Article by Bruce McMillan

Notice 58
Poem by David McCord

Student Resources
Books to Enjoy 60
Pictionary 62

Look at Me

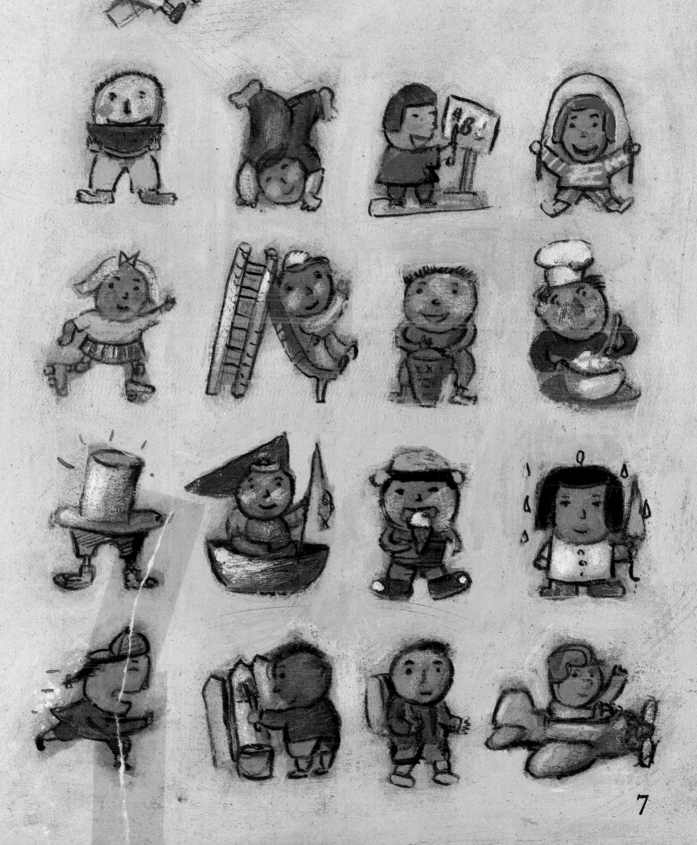

So Can I

by Allan Ahlberg and Colin McNaughton

I can brush my teeth.

I can write my name.

I can read a book.

I can carry the groceries.

I can brush my teeth and
write my name and
read a book and
carry the groceries.

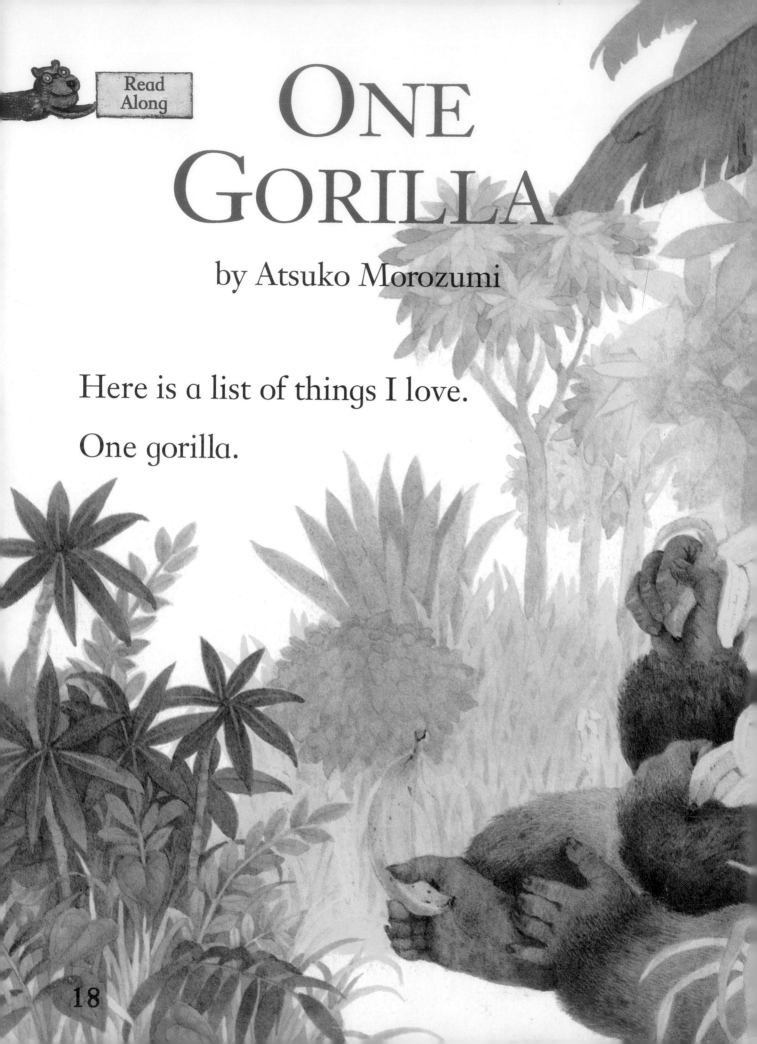

ONE GORILLA

by Atsuko Morozumi

Here is a list of things I love.

One gorilla.

20

Two butterflies among the flowers
and one gorilla.

Three parakeets in my house
and one gorilla.

22

Four squirrels in the woods
and one gorilla.

Five pandas in the snow
and one gorilla.

27

Six rabbits in a field
and one gorilla.

29

Seven frogs by the fence
and one gorilla.

Eight fish in the sea
and one gorilla.

Nine birds among the leaves
and one gorilla.

Ten cats in my garden
and one gorilla.

10 cats

9 birds

8 fish

7 frogs

6 rabbits

5 pandas

4 squirrels

3 parakeets

2 butterflies

But where is my gorilla?

Ah, there he is.

MY GORILLA

by Atsuko Morozumi

I used to live in London, England.

When I went to visit the London Zoo, I drew pictures of a very large gorilla who lived there. That gave me the idea for my book, One Gorilla.

42

To make all the other animals and things in my book look real, I drew from photographs and drawings.

I tried to hide the animals in my drawings. I used colors and many objects to make them hard to see.

Were you able to find them all?

Atsuko Morozumi

43

Mary Had a Little Lamb

by Sarah Josepha Hale

photo-illustrations by Bruce McMillan

Mary had a little lamb,

Its fleece was white as snow.

And everywhere that Mary went

The lamb was sure to go.

It followed her to school one day.

That was against the rule.

It made the children laugh and play

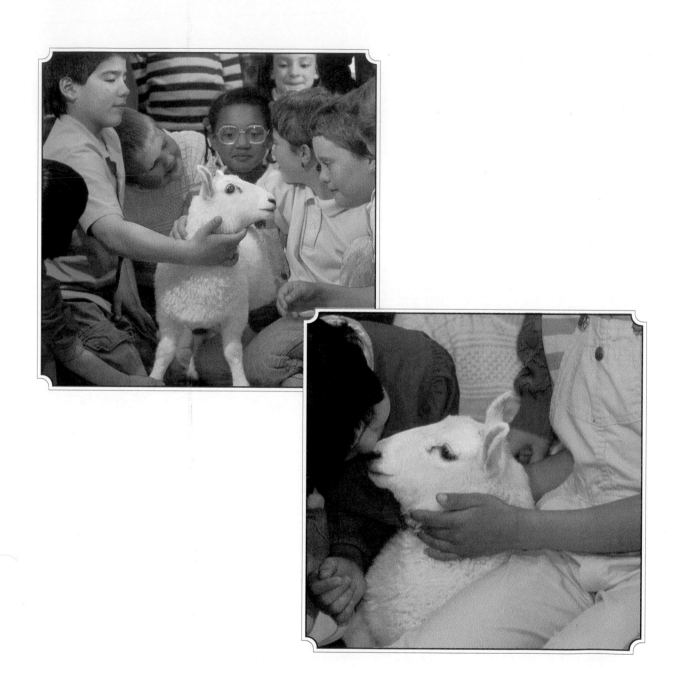

To see a lamb at school.

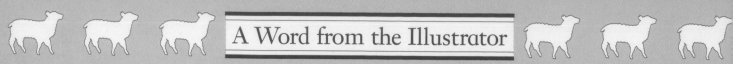 

Taking Pictures of Mary and Her Lamb

by Bruce McMillan

To take pictures for <u>Mary Had a Little Lamb</u>,
I needed someone to be Mary.
I found a pretty first-grade girl named
Sarah Jackson.

Second, I needed a lamb.
I found a frisky, young lamb named Argyle.

56

Photo: Benner McGee

Every day before I took any pictures,
Argyle got a bath. Why?
His fleece had to be "as white as snow."

I have a new sweater made from Argyle's wool.
Can you guess what color it is?

Notice

by David McCord

I have a dog,

I had a cat.

I've got a frog

Inside my hat.

Books to Enjoy

It Looked Like Spilt Milk
by Charles Shaw

What a funny-looking thing!
Is it a bird? Is it a flower?
Read and think about what
each shape might be.

Rise and Shine!
by Nancy White Carlstrom

Join in! Talk with animals all
around the farm and all through
the year.

Things I Like
by Anthony Browne

Monkey likes to ride a bike.
Find out if he likes to do any
of your favorite things.

A Playhouse for Monster

by Virginia Mueller
Illustrations by Lynn Munsinger

Monster has his playhouse all
to himself. Why isn't he happy?

Alphabeasts

by Durga Bernhard

You can find each animal.
Then all the letters from A to Z
make a puzzle for you too!

Everything Grows

by Raffi
Photo-illustrations
by Bruce McMillan

Everything grows and grows.
Brothers, sisters, babies too.

ride a bicycle

read a book

throw a ball

laugh

jump rope

63

Acknowledgments

Text
Page 8: *So Can I* by Allan Ahlberg and Colin McNaughton. Text copyright © 1985 by Allan Ahlberg. Illustrations copyright © 1985 by Colin McNaughton. Published in the United Kingdom by Walker Books Limited. Reprinted by permission.
Page 18: *One Gorilla* by Atsuko Morozumi. Text copyright © 1990 by Mathew Price. Illustrations copyright © 1990 by Atsuko Morozumi. Reprinted by permission of Mathew Price Ltd.
Page 42: "My Gorilla" by Atsuko Morozumi. Copyright © 1991 by Atsuko Morozumi.
Page 44: Photos from *Mary Had a Little Lamb* by Sara Josepha Hale copyright © 1990 by Bruce McMillan. All Rights Reserved. Reprinted by permission of Scholastic, Inc. Line drawing © 1990 by Bruce McMillan.
Page 56: "Taking Pictures of Mary and Her Lamb" by Bruce McMillan. Copyright © 1991 by Bruce McMillan.
Page 58: "Notice" from *One at a Time* by David McCord. Copyright © 1952 by David McCord. By permission of Little, Brown and Company.

Artists
Illustrations owned and copyrighted by the illustrator.
Andrew Shachat, cover, 1–7, 58–63
Colin McNaughton, 8–17
Atsuko Morozumi, 18–43
Bruce McMillan, 44, 56–57

Photographs
Page 43: Courtesy of Atsuko Morozumi.
Pages 44–56: Bruce McMillan
Page 57: Benner McGee (Courtesy of Bruce McMillan.)